APPLE SEEDS
&
SODA STRAWS

Some Love Charms and Legends

by Jean Ritchie

APPLE SEEDS
&
SODA STRAWS

Some Love Charms and Legends

illustrated by

Don Bolognese

New York   Henry Z. Walck, Inc.   1965

37338

LOVES ME – LOVES ME NOT

LOVES ME—LOVES ME NOT

THE surest way to find out if your sweetheart loves you is simply to ask, "Do you love me or not?" You might get an answer, then again, maybe you won't. Because there's a good chance that the one you like is as bashful as you are.

Anyway, most folks just aren't so outspoken about things like that. So, over the years, boys and girls all around the countryside have thought up ways to find out how their chosen sweethearts feel—without having to come right out and ask them.

Daisies Will Tell You

HERE is one way to find out if your sweetheart loves you that is known throughout the United States, and perhaps in all countries where daisies grow.

First pick a daisy, then pull the petals off one by one, saying "He loves me," as the first petal falls and "He loves me not," for the second petal and so on until all the petals are gone but one. If this last one falls on, "He loves me," then you can rest easy. He is as good as yours.

If you're not satisfied to know just this much, you may use this magic Kentucky rhyme on the daisy:

> He loves me,
> He don't,
> He'll marry me,
> He won't,
> He would if he could,
> But he can't.

Soda Straws and Apple Seeds

In the city, girls cannot always find a daisy when they need one, so they have had to think of something else. A drinking straw is a fine substitute.

After finishing your soda, use the straw to find out if the one you like, likes you. Hold the straw in your right hand and pinch the very bottom of it between the thumb and finger of your left hand. Then with your right thumb and finger, pinch the straw just above the first pinch. The first pinch is a "loves me" and the second a "loves me not." Work up to the top end of the straw, and the last pinch tells the truth.

Another substitute for daisies uses apple seeds. When you eat an apple, save all the seeds. Then count them off with a "loves me" or a "loves me not" for each in turn. The last seed is the answer. Both the soda straws and the apple seed can be used for the "Loves me, He don't, He'll marry me" rhyme.

Love Makes Hair Curl

TAKE one hair. A girl's hair is best, since it must be fairly long. Hold the root end firmly between thumb and forefinger of one hand. With the other hand, grasp the hair near the root between the thumbnail and forefinger, and pull quickly down the sides and off the end. If your sweetheart loves you, the hair will curl up tightly. If he likes you only a little, or hasn't made up his mind, the hair will curl only slightly. If the hair stays straight, then he cares nothing for you at all.

Tying a Knot in the Love Vine

THERE is a slender, pale gold-colored vine, named the Yellow Dodder, that grows in many parts of the United States. In the southern Appalachian Mountains it is called the love vine. The love vine is a parasite; it fastens itself onto and gets it food from another plant. The other plant is sometimes the sturdy, red-leafed, strong-smelling "hogweed." This plant is probably called hogweed because when it is young and tender, hogs eat it in great quantities, with grunts of pleasure and contented expressions.

The love vine curls lovingly around the stem of the hogweed, waving a graceful tendril above its head. The golden vine can tell you if your sweetheart likes you alone, or if he likes others as well. Break the vine about six or eight inches from the top. Tie a simple knot in the vine and try to draw the knot tight. If you can tie a good tight knot, your sweetheart is true—he has no other loves. If the love vine breaks before the knot is tight, he likes another, also. If this happens, tie the vine again. If the second knot holds, he likes you better than the other. If the second knot breaks—beware, for he likes two others at least as well as he likes you.

Advice: There is a trick to tying the knot. The love vine is brittle and breaks easily except at the top —its slimmest, youngest part. So, if you tie your knot near the end, you can almost always tighten it and get the answer you most wish to have.

Counting Bluebirds

BLUEBIRDS are fairly rare, and usually are seen just one at a time. Whenever you see a bluebird on a tree (redbirds count, too, but bluebirds are luckier), make a wish. If you can put the wish into words before the bluebird flies from that tree, your wish will come true.

But the exciting thing to watch for is something that you'll see, if you're lucky, about once or twice in your lifetime—a whole flock of bluebirds settling down to rest in one tree. I saw it just once. There must have been fifty of them, fluttering and twittering and wheeling over a young haw tree whose thorny branches were gleaming with bright red berries. Finally they decided to rest there, after much argument, and covered the branches like a bright blue cloud. For a very few seconds they rested, chattering and nibbling the red berries. Then on a sudden signal they rose, swooped to get their direction, and flashed away. The sight was so very beautiful, and unexpected, that I didn't think to count them until they were gone, and it was too late. But I'll pass on the magic here, in case *you* ever have the chance to use it.

As soon as the bluebirds alight, begin "counting" with this magic rhyme:

> One, you'll have sorrow,
> Two, you'll have joy;
> Three, take a journey,
> Four, get a boy;
> Five, receive silver,
> Six, receive gold—
> Seven's a secret that cannot be told.
> Eight, a love letter with promises three,
> Nine means your lover's as true as can be.

If the birds fly away before you say the words up through nine, your fortune will be told by whatever line of the rhyme you're saying when they fly. If they stay in the tree longer than it takes you to finish the rhyme, begin it again immediately and keep saying it until they fly away.

Your Wish Will Come True

THESE three charms can be used to make any sort of wish come true.

When you notice that your dress hem is turned up, quickly take the turned-up section between thumb and fingers, bend over, kiss that part of the hem and make a wish. Then lay a broom on the floor and jump over the broomstick. If your dress hem is still turned up after you have jumped, your wish will come true.

A chance to *will* him to love you will come your way if this happens: When you and another person—anyone—say exactly the same word or words at the same time, immediately hook the little fingers of your right hands together and silently make a wish, without speaking or laughing. Then, you begin the charm and the other person gives the responses.

First: Needles.
Second: Pins.
First: When a man marries,
Second: Trouble begins.
First: First thing he buys,
Second: Safety pins.
First: What goes up the chimney?
Second: Smoke
First: Touch something blue
Second: And your wish will come true.

The next time you take a walk or a drive in the country, remember this: If you meet, pass or see two piebald horses one after the other, whisper or think a wish, spit seven times, count to seven, and within seven days you will get your wish.

Love Is True as Oak

LOVE can be as true and strong as the heart of an oak tree—or as fragile as one of its leaves. The test, unfortunately, has to be made with the fragile leaf, but the results are often surprising.

Take a pin and scratch the initials of the one you love on an oak leaf. A maple, beech or other tree leaf will do, if there isn't an oak handy—although the oak leaf is the most dependable. After scratching good deep initials into the leaf, place the leaf face down in the bottom of your shoe and wear the shoe all day without taking it off for any reason. When you go to bed at night, don't look at the leaf and don't let anyone else see it. Put the shoe with the leaf in it underneath the head of your bed.

In the morning, as soon as you get out of bed, take the leaf out of the shoe and examine it carefully. If the boy's initials have become clearer, then he is true as the mighty oak tree itself, and you will some day marry him. If the initials have grown fainter, then his love for you is not true and strong, but will slowly fade away and vanish.

A Secret Test

To find out if someone loves you, hold out your left hand and ask him to see whether he can encircle your wrist with the thumb and forefinger of his right hand. The thumb and finger must make a complete circle, so that their tips can touch each other.

If his thumb and finger do not meet, he does not love you. If he has to stretch or struggle to make them touch, he has not yet made up his mind if he loves you. If the thumb and finger encircle your wrist with ease, you can have no doubt that he loves you.

Does He Think of Me?

MANY and many a time, a girl gets to wondering, when her sweetheart is away from her, "How often does he think of me?" There are some ways to tell just exactly which moments he is thinking about you. Here are the ones my mother passed on to me, from her experience:

When your apron strings come untied by themselves, your sweetheart is wishing he had some of your good cooking.

If you stumble while going upstairs, he is wanting to be with you to protect you.

Whenever you let the bread burn, he is thinking about you so strongly that it has taken your mind away. (The smell of burning bread usually brings it back again.)

If a hairpin or comb comes loose in your hair and falls out, you may be sure that he is thinking of you in a teasing way, and the next time he is with you, he will very likely ruffle up your hair.

When your left ear itches, his thoughts are loving. When your right ear itches, his thoughts are angry. When your nose itches, someone hungry is coming.

Advice: In case the hungry person who is coming *might* be your true love, it would be a good idea to bake a chocolate cake and have it ready.

Warm Hands, Warm Heart

We all used to walk to school at our little one-room schoolhouse in the Kentucky mountains. Some of the girls and boys had three or four or sometimes even five miles to walk to reach school.

On icy winter days, I remember tucking my mittened hands deep into my coat pockets as I ran down Elk Branch, because I knew that as soon as we all got inside the schoolhouse and were waiting for the "books" bell, the boys would be grabbing each girl's hands to see if they were warm or cold after being out in the weather. If a girl had ice-cold hands, they'd chant:

> Cold hands, cold heart,
> Dirty feet and no sweetheart!

I don't remember that there was a matching rhyme if the girl had warm hands. It was just, "Warm hands, warm heart," and the rest was understood. But I do remember that it was terribly important to get to school with warm hands. I did pretty well, too, since I lived only a quarter of a mile from the schoolhouse.

Bubbles in the Teacup

You will soon get a kiss if your cup of tea or cocoa has bubbles floating on the top.

If you can manage to drink the bubbles before they burst, then the person who will kiss you truly loves you.

Advice: Holding the pot a bit higher than usual when you pour your cup of tea or cocoa encourages bubbles, as does stirring vigorously with a spoon.

A Christmas Kiss

AT Christmas time, homes throughout our country and in many other lands are decorated with evergreens —pine boughs, holly wreaths, ivy chains, the Christmas tree, and always the sprig of mistletoe.

Tie it with a bit of red ribbon and hang it in a convenient place, a doorway that is much used or the middle of a room where people like to stand. Any girl caught standing under the mistletoe during the Christmas season may be kissed by any boy who finds her there.

One note of warning: Be sure that the sprig of mistletoe is burned on Twelfth Night. If this is not done, they say, then all the girls and boys who have kissed under it will never marry at all.

WHO LOVES ME?

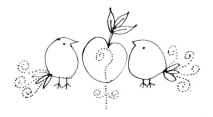

WHO LOVES ME?

MOST people, when they pull daisy petals or count apple seeds, have been able to find out whether or not their sweethearts love them. But many of them don't know who their sweethearts are, because they haven't chosen them yet. Perhaps you are one of these people. You have many dozens of friends, but none of them seem extra special. Or, maybe that special someone—your true love—is still a stranger to you.

Well, here are a few things you can do to find out just who this person will be. These are things which folks have believed in for hundreds of years. You try them, and, if you believe, you may find out who your true love is, or the name of the person you will marry, or what his occupation is. At the very least, you will find out the initial of his name.

A Snail On May Day Morning

GET up on May Day morning early, before sunrise, and walk until you find a snail. If it has a shell, you will marry a man who owns house and land. If you find a snail without a shell, you will marry a man who has no house.

Take the snail home and go into the kitchen. Get a smooth board, or use the top of the kitchen table or shelf. Sprinkle this smooth surface lightly with flour. Put the snail in the middle of the floured place and leave it for about an hour. When you come back, the snail will have written the name or the initial of the one who loves you best. Some say that the name on the board is the name of the one you will marry.

If the snail has written nothing in the hour, give it a little more time, but this means that you will not marry early. If, when you come back the second time, the snail has still written nothing, better try another charm.

Eggful of Salt

FIND a smooth brown egg, put it in a pot and boil it for twenty-one minutes. Peel the egg, and when it is cool, take a sharp knife and cut the egg in two. Then, take the yolk out of one of the halves, and fill the hole with salt.

Just before you go to bed for the night, eat the half-egg filled with salt, and don't drink any water.

The person who brings you a drink in your dreams will be your future husband.

For City Girls

HERE is a bit of magic to use—if you dare take the risk —to find out whom you will marry.

Count ninety-nine policemen, one postman, one bicycle. The next boy you speak to will be the man you will someday marry.

Ivy Charms

IN many countries of the world, the ivy plant is believed to be full of magic, especially in matters of love. This belief may have come from the legend of a beautiful young girl of ancient Greece, who danced before the god Dionysus. Her love for him was so great that she would not stop her joyful dance, until at last she fell dead at his feet. Dionysus was deeply moved, and decided that she should live forever. He changed her body into the ivy plant, which to this day shows its love by embracing whatever tree or rock is near.

Here is one of the charms to use with ivy. Put an ivy leaf inside your clothing, over your heart, and turn around three times. As you turn, repeat these words:

> Ivy, ivy, I love thee
> In my bosom I put thee
> The next young man that speaks to me
> My future husband he shall be.

From County Leitrim in Ireland comes another ivy charm, but there is no reason why it shouldn't work anywhere ivy grows. After darkness falls on Allhallows' Eve, gather ten ivy leaves, throw one away and put the other nine under your pillow. All this must be done without speaking. As soon as possible go to bed, and you will dream of the one you will love and marry.

Apple-Peel Initials

ANY time you are peeling a large apple, and wish to find out who your sweetheart is, do this:

Peel the apple very carefully, for if you break the peel before you reach the end, this charm won't work. When you reach the end, balance the end of the long peel between your knife blade and thumb for a moment, then fling it over your left shoulder.

If the peel breaks when it hits the floor, you have no sweetheart.

If it does not break, you will see that it has taken the shape of an initial—the one of your sweetheart.

What Dreams Can Tell You

SINCE time began, people have believed that the future can be foretold by their dreams. For instance, my grandmother used to tell us, "If you dream of death, that means someone you know will marry soon; if you dream of a wedding, you'll soon go to a funeral."

We children believed almost everything Grandmother told us, but I secretly thought that the second part of the saying was just superstition. The first part, about the marrying, bothered me too, because just *who* would marry was not made plain. We had other beliefs about dreams that I liked better, because they gave real facts.

When you are sleeping in a strange room, one in which you have never slept before, you will want to name the corners. Choose names of four people you really like. Stand in the middle of the room and point toward the corner nearest the door, saying aloud one of the names you have chosen. Turning clockwise round the room, point to the other three corners and give a name to each as you face it.

Be sure to remember which name belongs to which corner, because you will waken in the morning facing the corner named for the person you will marry.

Whenever you go to a wedding, save a small slice of the wedding cake and take it home with you.

That night slip the cake under your pillow when you go to sleep. You will dream about the one you will someday marry.

Run around a holly tree seven times to the left, then seven times to the right. Pick seven holly berries from the tree and put them underneath your pillow when you go to bed. You will dream of your future husband.

This one depends upon a stretch of good weather. If you can count seven stars each night for seven nights in a row, you will, on the seventh night, dream of the man who will be your husband.

When to Cut Fingernails

THERE is a folk-saying from Alabama and Georgia that explains why it is a good idea to cut your fingernails on a Saturday:

> Cut your nails on Monday, means news:
> On Tuesday, new shoes:
> On Wednesday, have far to go;
> On Thursday, be feeling low:
> On Friday, get a poke of money;
> On Saturday, you'll see your lover Sunday;
> Cut on Sunday, heed my warning—
> You'll see blood before the morning.

Bouncing the Ball

THERE are many rhymes to use when bouncing a ball, to find out things about your future mate. Here is a jingle which you can say to find out what his occupation will be.

In order to have this charm work, you must say it while standing on one foot and bouncing the ball:

> Tinker, tailor, soldier, sailor,
> Rich man, poor man, beggarman, thief,
> Squire, baby, gypsy, king,
> That's the one to marry me.

When you "miss" with the ball, the name you are saying on the missed bounce is the sort of person who will be your sweetheart.

But, if the foot you are holding in the air touches the floor during the chant, the spell is broken and you must begin all over again!

SOME SIGNS OF TROUBLE

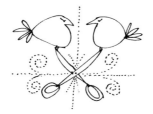

SOME SIGNS OF TROUBLE

IF you dream that you had a quarrel with your sweetheart, and you tell the dream before breakfast, it will come true.

If you lose his picture, you will soon have a serious quarrel with him, and—unless the picture is found or replaced right away—you may lose him.

If a boy and a girl wash their hands in the same water and don't spit to break the spell, they will fight.

If a girl makes the tea too weak, her sweetheart's love is weakening.

If your true love happens to hand you a knife, a pair of scissors or a brooch, you must quickly hand him in return a knife of some sort. Otherwise this foretells the end of your love for each other.

When stirring a drink:
    Stir with a spoon, life's in tune;
    Stir with a fork, dogs will bark;
    Stir with a knife, stir for strife.

You may expect a great deal of trouble with your sweetheart if you find two knives crossed at your place at the table.

BE MY VALENTINE

BE MY VALENTINE

ONE of the nicest ways of saying, "I love you," is to send a roses-and-lace-and-ribbons love letter on the fourteenth of February, St. Valentine's Day.

Just where this custom originated is hard to say. Long ago, it was thought to be good luck to give a bouquet of forget-me-nots to a friend starting on a journey on February twenty-ninth. Then, the custom grew into that of exchanging forget-me-not bouquets among friends, on that day, even though no journey was made.

In medieval England, the young people, noting that birds chose their mates in this early spring season, began to make up games in which each girl would choose a special friend or sweetheart (later, a "valentine") by drawing a name from among the names of the boys in her circle of friends. Sometimes this choosing was not done by drawing names, but it would be understood that the first boy she met when she walked out on February fourteenth would kiss and "claim" her, and she would be his special friend for one year.

February 14th was probably settled upon, and the name "valentine" chosen (to mean either love letter or sweetheart), because the feast day of St.

Valentine fell upon that day. He was a kindly man whom the people loved and he later became known as the patron of lovers.

Nowadays, we send many valentines, expressing different degrees of our feelings of friendliness and love. It is a joyful, light-hearted holiday, full of good feeling and happy wishes. And best of all, it is the one day in the year when you can feel perfectly free to say, "I love you."

DATE DUE

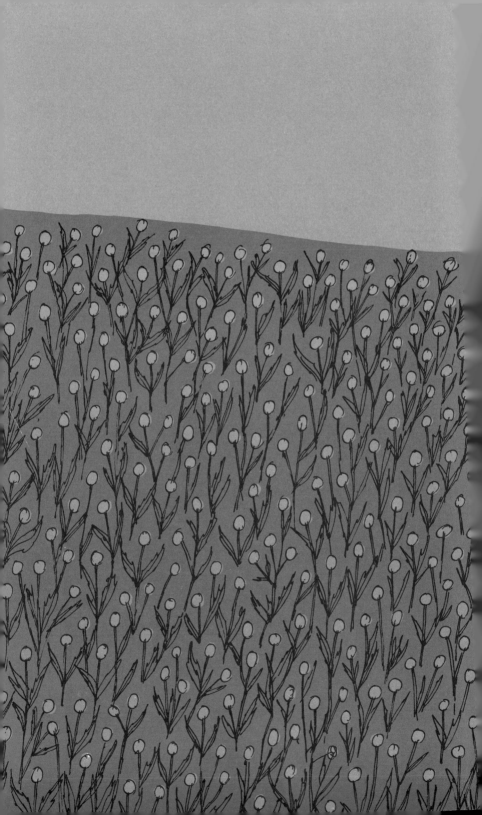